Editor
Eric Migliaccio

Editor in Chief
Ina Massler Levin, M.A.

Cover Designer
Karen J. Goldfluss, M.S. Ed.

Cover Artist
Barb Lorseyedi

Creative Director
Karen J. Goldfluss, M.S. Ed.

Imaging
James Edward Grace
Craig Gunnell

CD Application Programmer
Charles Payne

Publisher
Mary D. Smith, M.S. Ed.

Teacher Created Resources
TCR 3610

Interactive Learning

for All INTERACTIVE WH

Paragraph Editing

CORRELATED TO COMMON CORE STANDARDS

Do you have a pet? I have an orange goldfish for a pet. It is shiny, so i named it Sparkle. I like to watch sparkle swim around her Bowl.

* Developed for ALL Interactive Whiteboards
* 100 ready-to-edit paragraphs to practice and review grammar, punctuation, and spelling
* Includes Common Core State Standards

Teacher Created Resources

Teacher Created Resources
6421 Industry Way
Westminster, CA 92683
www.teachercreated.com
ISBN: 978-1-4206-3610-4

Made in U.S.A.

Table of Contents

Introduction

Imagine a classroom tool that could make grammar and spelling exciting and engaging for your students. *Paragraph Editing* is a program that has been designed to do all of this and more. Compatible with all interactive whiteboards, *Paragraph Editing* offers the many advantages of touchscreen technology and allows your students to participate in learning like never before.

Each *Paragraph Editing* CD comes loaded with the paragraphs from this book. The paragraphs are divided into 25 units, with new grammar rules incorporated into each of the first 15 units. In this way, grammar, punctuation, and spelling concepts are introduced and then reinforced in a systematic manner, allowing students to practice each concept before learning new ones. The final 10 units of each book and CD offer a cumulative reinforcement of all of the rules and concepts previously learned.

These paragraphs can be accessed and printed from the CD or copied from the book. They can be done as in-class work or assigned as homework. Corrections to these parapraphs can then be made on individual computers or on an interactive whiteboard in front of the class. All it takes is a finger or a special pen, depending on the interactive board you use. You and your students can correct the sentences in these ways:

- ☞ by writing and drawing directly onto the interactive whiteboard
- ☞ by grabbing punctuation stamps built into the program and dragging them over the corresponding errors

An array of buttons and menus allows you to do (and undo) every correction quickly and easily and in six custom colors. Best of all, it takes just one quick click of a button for teachers and students to see the correct answers. And, as an added teaching tool, another touch of a button will show students the locations of the paragraph's errors without revealing the actual answers.

In addition to the paragraphs included on the CD, the *Paragraph Editing* program allows you to create and save thousands of custom paragraphs. The program can even make incorrect versions of your custom creations by adding errors for you. Teachers can use this tool to tap into their class's creativity with student-generated paragraphs and peer-editing exercises.

Common Core State Standards

The activities in this book meet one or more of the following Common Core State Standards. For more information about the Common Core State Standards, go to *http://www.corestandards.org/.*

Reading Standards: Foundational Skills

Print Concepts

Standard 1: RF.1.1 Demonstrate understanding of the organization and basic features of print.

- RF.1.1a: Recognize the distinguishing features of a sentence.

Phonics and Word Recognition

Standard 3: RF.1.3 Know and apply grade-level phonics and word analysis skills in decoding words.

- RF.1.3g: Recognize and read grade-appropriate irregularly spelled words.

Fluency

Standard 4: RF.1.4 Read with sufficient accuracy and fluency to support comprehension.

- RF.1.4a: Read grade-level text with purpose and understanding.
- RF.1.4c: Use context to confirm or self-correct word recognition and understanding, rereading as necessary.

Language Standards

Conventions of Standard English

Standard 1: L.1.1 Demonstrate command of the conventions of standard English grammar and usage when writing or speaking.

- L.1.1b: Use common, proper, and possessive nouns.
- L.1.1c: Use singular and plural nouns with matching verbs in basic sentences.
- L.1.1d: Use personal, possessive, and indefinite pronouns.
- L.1.1e: Use verbs to convey a sense of past, present, and future.
- L.1.1j: Produce and expand simple and compound declarative, interrogative, imperative, and exclamatory sentences in response to prompts.

Standard 2: L.1.2 Demonstrate command of the conventions of standard English capitalization, punctuation, and spelling when writing.

- L.1.2a: Capitalize dates and names of people.
- L.1.2b: Use end punctuation for sentences.
- L.1.2c: Use commas in dates and to separate single words in a series.
- L.1.2d: Use conventional spelling for words with common spelling patterns and for frequently occurring irregular words.

About the CD

The real flexibility and interactivity of the *Paragraph Editing* program shine through in the resources included on the CD.

☞ Install the CD

Just pop the CD that accompanies this book into your PC or Mac, and you and your students can begin editing paragraphs at individual computers or on the interactive whiteboard in your classroom.

> **Quick Tip:** Step-by-step installation instructions and some troubleshooting tips are provided in the "ReadMe" file on the CD.

☞ The Main Menu

Once you have installed the CD, the Main Menu will appear on your computer screen or interactive whiteboard.

> **Quick Tip:** The Main Menu will open up in full-screen mode. If you wish to resize the Main Menu screen, hit the ESC button. This will allow you to adjust it as needed.

From the Main Menu, you can access all of the features and resources available in the program. To get a detailed explanation of these features, click on the Guide button. This will take you to the *Paragraph Editing* User's Guide.

☞ The User's Guide

Everything you need to know in order to use and operate the *Paragraph Editing* CD and program can be found in the User's Guide. This is also where you will find a useful one-page handout of the editing symbols used in the program. These marks are available as punctuation stamps on the editing screen for each sentence.

Main Menu Screen

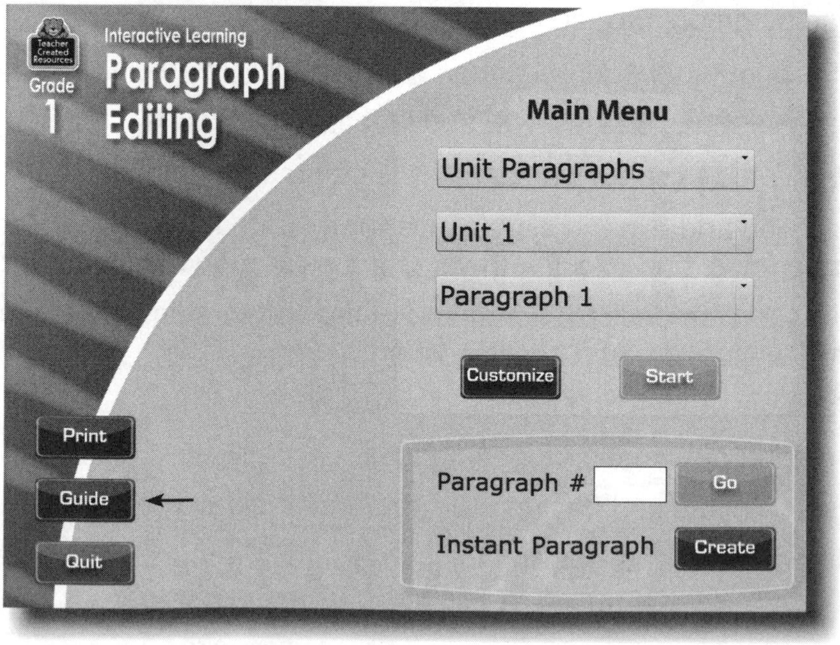

About the CD *(cont.)*

The User's Guide on the CD contains a lot of important and helpful information. However, you may wish to immediately begin editing paragraphs with your students. The following Quick-Start Guide will help you do just that.

Quick-Start Guide for Editing Paragraphs

1. **Launch the Program:** Load the CD and launch the program. If needed, follow the installation instructions given in the "ReadMe" file on the CD.

2. **Click the Start Button:** You can access the **Start** button from the **Main Menu** screen. (See the graphic to the right.) This will take you directly to the editing screen. (See the graphic at the bottom of the page.)

Main Menu
Unit Paragraphs
Unit 1
Paragraph 1
Customize
Start

3. **Edit the Paragraph:** Write, draw, or paint directly onto the screen. You may also use the punctuation stamps located on either side of the screen. Grab, drag, and drop these stamps onto, above, or below the word to correct the errors.

4. **Check Your Work:** Click on the **Show Errors** button to give your students hints about where the errors can be found in the paragraph. Click on the **Show Correct** button to reveal the correct version of the paragraph.

5. **Edit a New Paragraph:** Click on the **Next** button to continue the editing lesson with a new paragraph.

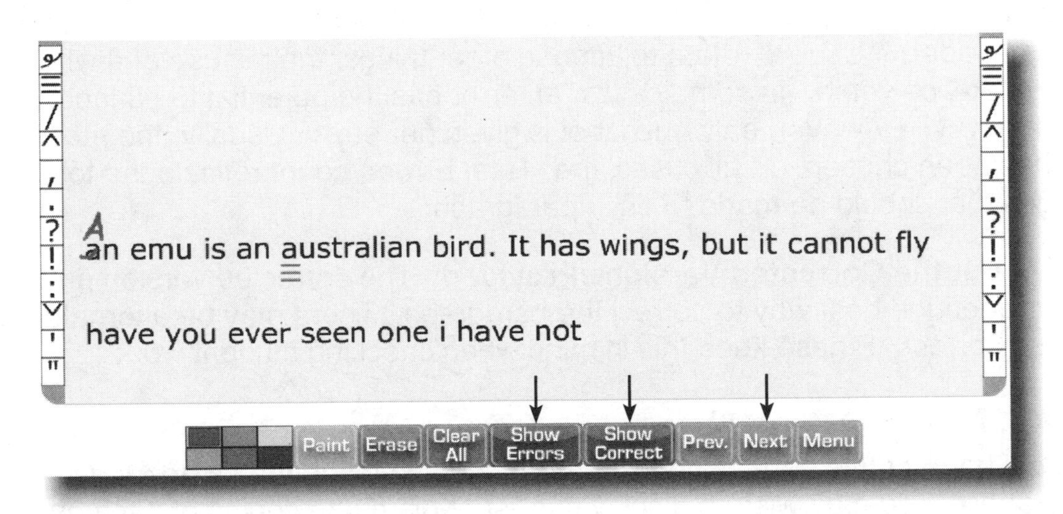

About the Book

There are two main components to the *Paragraph Editing* program: a book and a CD. These two parts were designed to be complementary, but they can also be used independently of one another. This 112-page book contains the following features:

☞ **Common Core State Standards (page 3)**

The grammar rules and concepts reviewed in this book meet Common Core State Standards for grade-level appropriateness.

☞ **Tips for Using the CD (pages 4–5)**

These two pages include tips for getting started with the CD that accompanies this book.

☞ **Grammar Rules (pages 7–11)**

This book includes a list of the punctuation, capitalization, and usage rules students will need to know in order to correct the paragraphs. New rules are introduced in each of the first 15 units, allowing students to learn increasingly difficult grammar concepts at a measured pace, while reviewing the ones they have previously learned. The final 10 units serve as a cumulative review of the rules learned in the first 15 units.

☞ **Ready-To-Be-Edited Paragraphs (pages 12–111)**

On each even-numbered page of this section, there are two error-filled paragraphs. (In all, this book contains a total of 100 unique paragraphs.) These paragraphs contain plenty of space between lines so students may add editing marks and rewrite incorrectly spelled words. Copy these pages for use as in-class assignments or send them home as homework.

On the odd-numbered pages that follow, the corrected versions of the paragraphs are given. The revisions are shown in gray, and a summary of the errors that can be found in each paragraph is provided.

Note About the Summary of Errors: The terms used in this list are meant to help you quickly locate specific types of errors. Many terms refer to both the omission and the misuse of that element. *Examples:* The term "Periods" is given when a period is missing and also when one is used incorrectly (in place of a question mark, for example). "Capitalization" is a broad term used to refer to any instance where a capital or lowercase letter is needed. "Usage" refers to, among other things, the misuse of *a* when *an* is needed, or vice versa. In some cases, an error has the potential to be labeled in more than one way. However, only one label is given per error. Usually, the most specific term has been chosen. In all cases, the "Total Errors" count reflects the total number of changes that should be made to each paragraph.

Note About the Corrected Versions Provided: The corrected version provided shows what is often the best way to correct the paragraph. There may be alternate ways that are also correct. Please keep this in mind when checking student work.

☞ **Editing Marks (page 112)**

The final page of this book contains a full list of the editing marks needed to correct the paragraphs. You may wish to display this list or distribute copies of it to your students.

Grammar Rules

The following pages include most of the grammar, usage, and punctuation rules students will need to know to edit the paragraphs in this book. The units in which these rules are applicable are listed in parentheses after each rule.

Rule 1: A *sentence* is a group of words that tells a complete thought. Capitalize the first word in a sentence. A *statement* is a sentence that tells something. Put a period at the end of a telling sentence. **(Units 1–30)**

- **My dog is black.**

Rule 2: A *question* is a sentence that asks something. Put a question mark at the end of an asking sentence. **(Units 1–30)**

- **Do you have a pet?**

Rule 3: Always capitalize the word *I*. **(Units 1–30)**

- **Scott and I are friends.**

Rule 4: *Nouns* are words that name people, places, things, and ideas. **(Units 1–30)**

- **The doctor sat in his office.**
- **Honesty is the best policy.**

Rule 5: *Proper nouns* name specific people, places, things, and ideas. A proper noun begins with a capital letter. *Common nouns* are not specific. A common noun *does not* begin with a capital letter. **(Units 1–30)**

- **That dog is named Max.** (common noun = *dog*; proper noun = *Max*)
- **Did Mom and Dad see Steve's dad at the mall?**
- **The Johnson family went to New York on vacation.**

Rule 6: An *exclamation* is a sentence that shows feeling. It ends with an exclamation mark. A *command* is a sentence that tells someone to do something. It ends with a period or an exclamation mark. (**Units 2–30**).

- **We won the game!**
- **Get out of the street!**
- **Please print your name.**

Rule 7: A *run-on sentence* has two complete thoughts that run into each other. Use a period or other end punctuation to divide these thoughts into two sentences. **(Units 2–30)**

- **I woke up late my alarm clock is broken.** (incorrect)
- **I woke up late. My alarm clock is broken.** (correct)

Grammar Rules *(cont.)*

Rule 8: Capitalize the days of the week, months of the year, and holidays. Do not capitalize seasons of the year. **(Units 2–30)**

- **Is Memorial Day on a Monday in May?**
- **My favorite season is spring.**

Rule 9: A *colon* is used between the hour and minutes when writing the time of day. **(Units 3–30)**

- **We went to school at 8:00.**

Rule 10: An *abbreviation* is a short form of a word. Capitalize name titles and put a period after ones that have been shortened into an abbreviation. Also capitalize and put a period after initials, which are letters used instead of a full name. Do not capitalize *a.m.* or *p.m.* **(Units 3–30)**

- **The shop is owned by Mr. Payne.**
- **My dentist is Dr. Anna Lee.**
- **The author is J.P. Wilson.**
- **Dinner will be served at 6:30 p.m.**

Rule 11: Use a comma to separate the day and year or to separate the day and month. Use a comma to separate a city and state or country. **(Units 5–30)**

- **She was born on Thursday, November 2, 2006.**
- **Andrea flew from Houston, Texas, to Paris, France.**

Rule 12: A series is a list of three or more items. Use a comma to separate three or more words or groups of words in a series. **(Units 6–30)**

- **Would you rather have pizza, pasta, or a hamburger?**

Rule 13: A *singular noun* names one person, place, thing, or idea. A *plural noun* names more than one person, place, thing, or idea. Add *s* to most nouns to make them plural. Add *es* to words that end in *s, ch, sh, x,* and *z*. **(Units 7–30)**

- **I have two small dogs and one big dog.**
- **I see one blue dish and two red dishes.**

Grammar Rules *(cont.)*

Rule 14: Use *a* or *an* before singular nouns. Use *a* before words that begin with a consonant sound. Use *an* before words that begin with a vowel or vowel sound. **(Units 7–30)**

- **He ate a piece of toast and an egg an hour before school began.**

Rule 15: Nouns that end in the letter *y* have special rules for making plurals. If the word ends with a vowel followed by *y*, just add *s*. If the word ends with a consonant followed by *y*, change the *y* to *i* and add *es*. **(Units 8–30)**

- **Dad put his keys in his coat pocket.**
- **I went to three birthday parties in June.**

Rule 16: Nouns that end in *f* or *fe* also have a special rule for making plurals. In most words, change the *f* to *v* and add *es*. **(Units 8–30)**

- **I found six butter knives and one bread knife in the drawer.**
- **One calf has black spots. Two calves have brown spots.**

Rule 17: A *possessive noun* shows ownership. Use an *apostrophe* and an *s* (*'s*) after a noun to show that something belongs to one person or thing. To form the plural possessive of a plural noun that ends in *s*, add only an apostrophe. If the plural noun does not end in *s*, add an apostrophe and an *s*. **(Units 9–30)**

- **Beth's guitar is sitting next to Jess's drum set.**
- **Both of his brothers' bikes are blue.**
- **We visited the children's library yesterday.**

Rule 18: A *pronoun* is a word that is used in place of a noun. Use the pronouns *we/us, she/he, her/him,* and *they/them* correctly. **(Units 10–30)**

Use "we" when you and others are doing something.

Use "she/he/they" when a person or group that doesn't include you is doing something.

Use "us" when something happens to you and others.

Use "her/him/them" when something is happening to a person or a group that doesn't include you.

- **We went to school.**
- **He is riding the bike.**
- **Sam gave him a ride.**
- **They gave the trophy to us.**
- **She will cook dinner for them.**
- **Bill took her to the movie.**

Grammar Rules *(cont.)*

Rule 19: Use the pronouns *I* and *me* correctly. Use the pronoun *I* when you are doing something. Use the pronoun "me" when something happens to you. **(Units 10–30)**

- **Mom and I went to Hawaii.**
- **She waved to Bob and me.**

Rule 20: The *verb* often shows the action of the sentence. When the subject of the sentence is singular, an *s* or *es* is usually added to the verb (except with the pronouns *I* or *you*.) When the subject is plural, an *s* is not added to the verb. **(Units 11–30)**

- **Ryan eats a lot of food. Eric and Bob eat more food.**
- **You eat broccoli for lunch. I do not eat broccoli.**
- **The school fixes lunch for us. They fix lunch for us every day.**

Rule 21: The verbs *am, are, is, was,* and *were* are forms of the word *be*. They are not action words. Instead, they tell what someone or something is like. **(Units 11–30)**

Use "am" with the word "I."

Use "is" and "are" when talking about what is happening now.

Use "was" and "were" when talking about things that have already happened.

Use "is" and "was" when talking about one person, place, thing, or idea.

Use "are" and "were" when talking about more than one person, place, thing, or idea, and with the word "you."

- **I am six years old.**
- **You are older than I am.**
- **Jim is seven years old.**
- **Last year, Jim was six.**
- **Kate and Nate are eight.**
- **They were seven last year.**

Rule 22: A *present-tense verb* shows action that happens now. A *past-tense verb* tells about an action that already happened. Add *ed* to most verbs to form the past tense. In addition to *s* and *es,* the ending *ing* can also be added to present-tense verbs. If the verb has a single vowel and ends with a consonant, the last consonant is usually doubled before adding *ed* or *ing.* If the word ends with a silent *e*, drop the final *e* before adding *ed* or *ing.* **(Units 12–30)**

- **The car stops here now. It also stopped here yesterday. Will it be stopping here every day?**
- **I wave goodbye. I waved to everybody. I am waving my hand.**

Grammar Rules *(cont.)*

Rule 23: If a verb ends with a consonant and *y*, change the *y* to *i* and add *es* to form the present-tense verb. If a verb ends with a consonant and *y*, change the *y* to *i* and add *ed* to form a past-tense verb. **(Units 13–30)**

- **Each team tries to win.**
- **I tried to hit a home run.**

Rule 24: The past tense of some verbs is made by changing the spelling. **(Units 14–30)**

- **Last week my dog ran away.** *(run)*
- **He bought some milk at the store.** *(buy)*
- **He drew a picture in art class.** *(draw)*

Rule 25: A *homophone* is a word that sounds the same as another word but has a different spelling and/or meaning. Be careful not to confuse these and other misused words, such as *are/our* and *it's/its.* **(Units 15–30)**

- **I can see the ship out on the sea.**
- **Scott ate eight donuts for breakfast!**
- **Are you coming to our house today?**
- **It's time to give the dog its bath.**

Name: ______________________________ Date: ____________________

Unit 1
Paragraph 1

Ann cuts the page. Bill adds red and blue paper to the page Ann and bill make a picture they hang it on the wall

Unit 1
Paragraph 2

Bob likes to fish He has a pole and a hook. do you know what happens next. Bob catches a fish. He lets it go Then bob goes home.

Ann cuts the page. Bill adds red and blue paper to the page Ann and bill make a picture they hang it on the wall

Unit 1 • Paragraph 1 Errors

Capitalization 2
Periods. 3

Total Errors: 5

Bob likes to fish He has a pole and a hook. do you know what happens next. Bob catches a fish. He lets it go Then bob goes home.

Unit 1 • Paragraph 2 Errors

Capitalization 2
Periods. 2
Question Marks. 1

Total Errors: 5

Name: ______________________ Date: ______________________

jane and Jill wanted to race. Jane ran faster than jill. Can you guess who won the race. Jane won the race They both laughed and had funn.

The sun is a big star It gives light and heat to earth. the sun is always shining. Sometimes we cannot see it. Sometimes it iss shining on the other side of the world Sometimes it is hiding behind the Clouds.

jane and Jill wanted to race. Jane ran faster than jill. Can you guess who won the race, Jane won the race They both laughed and had funn.

fun

Unit 1 • Paragraph 3 Errors

Capitalization 2
Periods......... 1
Question Marks......... 1
Spelling 1

Total Errors: 5

The sun is a big star It gives light and heat to earth. the sun is always shining. Sometimes we cannot see it. Sometimes it iss shining on the other side of the world Sometimes it is hiding behind the Clouds.

Unit 1 • Paragraph 4 Errors

Capitalization 3
Periods......... 2
Spelling 1

Total Errors: 6

Name: ______________________ Date: ______________________

Do you have a pet. I have an orange goldfish for a pet It is shiny, so i named it Sparkle. I like to watch sparkle swim around her Bowl.

I hav a pet dog named lady. Lady was born last Winter. She was born on the tenth of november. We will celebrate her first birthday on tuesday. Do you think that is silly.

Do you have a pet. I have an orange goldfish for a pet It is shiny, so i named it Sparkle. I like to watch sparkle swim around her Bowl.

Unit 2 • Paragraph 5 Errors

Capitalization 3
Periods.......... 1
Question Marks.......... 1

Total Errors: 5

I hav a pet dog named lady. Lady was born last Winter. She was born on the tenth of november. We will celebrate her first birthday on tuesday. Do you think that is silly.

Unit 2 • Paragraph 6 Errors

Capitalization 4
Question Marks.......... 1
Spelling 1

Total Errors: 6

Name: ______________________________ Date: ____________________

there are five very big lakes between america and canada. They can be seen from space. One is called Lake superior. It is the second biggest lake in the world? Wow, that is a giant lake.

Unit 2
Paragraph
8

Tim was att the zoo He was standing close to the tiger Cage. He was standing too close. Watch out. Tigers can bite you. tim moved away from the cage

there are five very big lakes between america and canada. They can be seen from space. One is called Lake superior. It is the second biggest lake in the world? Wow, that is a giant lake.

Unit 2 • Paragraph 7 Errors

Capitalization 4
Exclamation Points......... 1
Periods......... 1

Total Errors: 6

Tim was att the zoo He was standing close to the tiger Cage. He was standing too close. Watch out. Tigers can bite you. tim moved away from the cage

Unit 2 • Paragraph 8 Errors

Capitalization 2
Exclamation Points......... 1
Periods......... 2
Spelling 1

Total Errors: 6

Name: ______________________________ Date: ____________________

Unit 3
Paragraph
9

There once was a bigg frog named Mr Hoppy. He lived in a pond? he liked to eat bugs. He liked to hopp. Hopping was his favorite thing to do

It is the first Day of school. Mrs Flame wants us to learn the name of each boy and girl in our class She showed us how to play a game to learn names. i learned that three other boyys have the same name as I do My name is tom.

There once was a bigg frog named Mr. Hoppy. He lived in a pond? he liked to eat bugs. He liked to hopp. Hopping was his favorite thing to do.

Unit 3 • Paragraph 9 Errors

Capitalization 1
Periods 3
Spelling 2

Total Errors: 6

It is the first Day of school. Mrs. Flame wants us to learn the name of each boy and girl in our class. She showed us how to play a game to learn names. i learned that three other ~~boyys~~ boys have the same name as I do. My name is tom.

Unit 3 • Paragraph 10 Errors

Capitalization 3
Periods 3
Spelling 1

Total Errors: 7

Name: ______________________ Date: ______________________

Mike wakes upp at 6:30 a m. He showers and gets dressed. he eats breakfast and brushes his teeth. Hee meets me at the bus at 7.30. Mike and i get to school by 745.

Unit 3
Paragraph
12

What will u do this summer. I plan on going to the beach a lot. i also want to go swimming at Mr and mrs. Hill's house. They have a big pool. I luv swimming in the Summer.

Mike wakes upp at 6:30 a m. He showers and gets dressed. he eats breakfast and brushes his teeth. Hee meets me at the bus at 7,30. Mike and i get to school by 745.

Unit 3 • Paragraph 11 Errors

Capitalization	2
Colons	2
Periods	1
Spelling	2

Total Errors: 7

What will u do this summer, I plan on going to the beach a lot. i also want to go swimming at Mr and mrs. Hill's house. They have a big pool. I luv swimming in the Summer.

Unit 3 • Paragraph 12 Errors

Capitalization	3
Periods	1
Question Marks	1
Spelling	2

Total Errors: 7

Name: ______________________ Date: ______________

Mrs wilson likes clouds. She likes to look at them while she eats her Lunch She sees shapes in the clouds. the shapes look like animals. Have you ever seen a cloud shaped like an animal.

Unit 4
Paragraph
14

Do you want to see that new Movie. It starts at 330. That means that we need to leave home by 245 i want to get there before they turn off the lights?

Mrs wilson likes clouds. She likes to look at them while she eats her Lunch She sees shapes in the clouds. the shapes look like animals. Have you ever seen a cloud shaped like an animal.

Unit 4 • Paragraph 13 Errors

Capitalization 3
Periods......... 2
Question Marks......... 1

Total Errors: 6

Do you want to see that new Movie. It starts at 330. That means that we need to leave home by 245 i want to get there before they turn off the lights?

Unit 4 • Paragraph 14 Errors

Capitalization 2
Colons 2
Periods......... 2
Question Marks......... 1

Total Errors: 7

Name: ______________________ Date: ______________________

School starts at 8:00 a m. Lunch is served at 1215 p m School usually ends at 300. Mr jones always forgets to look at the clock. he is still teaching us when the bell rings.

Unit 4
Paragraph
16

My favorite TV show comes on at 730 It is a show about animals. I like to watch it with aunt sue and my two dogs? My Aunt takes care of sick animals. She hass helped rover and Scruffy many times.

School starts at 8:00 a m. Lunch is served at 1215 p m School usually ends at 300. Mr jones always forgets to look at the clock. he is still teaching us when the bell rings.

Unit 4 • Paragraph 15
Errors

Capitalization	2
Colons	2
Periods	4

Total Errors: 8

My favorite TV show comes on at 730 It is a show about animals. I like to watch it with aunt sue and my two dogs? My Aunt takes care of sick animals. She hass helped rover and Scruffy many times.

Unit 4 • Paragraph 16
Errors

Capitalization	4
Colons	1
Periods	2
Spelling	1

Total Errors: 8

Name: ______________________ Date: ______________________

Mrs anna May Watson was born on april 14 1932. She is over 80 years old She has lived in Athens Georgia, her whole life. We have been friends wth her for a long time.

Unit 5
Paragraph
18

Memorial day will be celebrated on may 31 this year. There will be a parade in the town of Atkins Iowa in honor of the Holiday. The band from Oak Ave high School will be marching in the parade

Mrs anna May Watson was born on april 14 1932. She is over 80 years old She has lived in Athens Georgia, her whole life. We have been friends ~~wth~~ with her for a long time.

Unit 5 • Paragraph 17 Errors

Capitalization	2
Commas	2
Periods	2
Spelling	1

Total Errors: 7

Memorial day will be celebrated on may 31 this year. There will be a parade in the town of Atkins Iowa in honor of the Holiday. The band from Oak Ave high School will be marching in the parade

Unit 5 • Paragraph 18 Errors

Capitalization	4
Commas	2
Periods	2

Total Errors: 8

Name: ______________________________ Date: ______________________________

My friend was born in Cincinnati ohio, but he grew up in anaheim California. I first met him on October 31 2009. I remember the date because it was halloween. He was dresssed up as a ghost. I don't remember what costume i wore.

do you know what happened on July 20 1969 That was the day a persun first walked on the mooon. An astronaut named Neil armstrong was the person who did it. Would you like to walk on the moon some day.

My friend was born in Cincinnati ohio, but he grew up in anaheim California. I first met him on October 31 2009. I remember the date because it was halloween. He was ~~dresssed~~ dressed up as a ghost. I don't remember what costume i wore.

Unit 5 • Paragraph 19 Errors

Capitalization 4
Commas. 3
Spelling 1

Total Errors: 8

do you know what happened on July 20 1969? That was the day a ~~persun~~ person first walked on the ~~mooon~~ moon. An astronaut named Neil armstrong was the person who did it. Would you like to walk on the moon some day?

Unit 5 • Paragraph 20 Errors

Capitalization 2
Commas. 1
Question Marks. 2
Spelling 2

Total Errors: 7

Name: ______________________ Date: ______________

one bug leaves a bad smell wherever it goes. it is the stinkbug Stinkbugs can be green gray brown, or red. Their bad odor protects themm from enemies.

Unit 6
Paragraph
22

My friend Jose garcia likes to play soccer on saturdays. He is the best player in our school i would rather play basketball baseball or hockey. Which sport do you like to play.

one bug leaves a bad smell wherever it goes. it is the stinkbug Stinkbugs can be green gray brown, or red. Their bad odor protects themm from enemies.

Unit 6 • Paragraph 21 Errors

Capitalization	2
Commas	2
Periods	1
Spelling	1

Total Errors: 6

My friend Jose garcia likes to play soccer on saturdays. He is the best player in our school i would rather play basketball baseball or hockey. Which sport do you like to play.

Unit 6 • Paragraph 22 Errors

Capitalization	3
Commas	2
Periods	1
Question Marks	1

Total Errors: 7

Name: ______________________ Date: ______________________

Unit 6
Paragraph 23

Jason likes to go to the zoo. He sees the monkeys the birrds and the tigers his favorite aminal is the giraffe. Sometimes he gets to feed the ducks. There is always something fun for jason to do at the zoo?

Unit 6
Paragraph 24

the farm is a fun place to visit You can see horses cows and pigs on the farm. Farmers work verry hard. They plant many crops so we can have food to eet. Would you like to be a Farmer.

Jason likes to go to the zoo. He sees the monkeys, the ~~birrds~~ birds, and the tigers. his favorite ~~aminal~~ animal is the giraffe. Sometimes he gets to feed the ducks. There is always something fun for jason to do at the zoo?

Unit 6 • Paragraph 23 Errors

Capitalization	2
Commas	2
Periods	2
Spelling	2

Total Errors: 8

the farm is a fun place to visit. You can see horses, cows, and pigs on the farm. Farmers work ~~verry~~ very hard. They plant many crops so we can have food to ~~eet~~ eat. Would you like to be a Farmer.

Unit 6 • Paragraph 24 Errors

Capitalization	2
Commas	2
Periods	1
Question Marks	1
Spelling	2

Total Errors: 8

Name: ______________________ Date: ______________________

Billy had a birthday party billy invited 10 friend to his Party. They played many game. They ate cake and ice cream Billy opened ten great present. What a super day

We need rivers. River bring water from mountain to oceans. they also bring water to lakes. Snow falls on the mountanns. Then it melts The water runs dowwn the mountain. it becomes a river?

Billy had a birthday party billy invited 10 friend to his Party. They played many game. They ate cake and ice cream Billy opened ten great present. What a super day

Unit 7 • Paragraph 25 Errors

Capitalization	2
Exclamation Points	1
Periods	2
Plurals	3

Total Errors: 8

We need rivers. River bring water from mountain to oceans. they also bring water to lakes. Snow falls on the ~~mountanns.~~ mountains Then it melts The water runs ~~dowwn~~ down the mountain. it becomes a river?

Unit 7 • Paragraph 26 Errors

Capitalization	2
Periods	2
Plurals	2
Spelling	2

Total Errors: 8

Name: ______________________________ Date: ____________________

One kind of worm from South america is eight feet long Have you ever seen such a huge worm. Yuck. Most worm are only a few inchs long. Some are less than a inch long

Jane has many job around the house. She walks the dog twice a weeek. She washes the dishs after breakfast every saturday morning. She moves all three trashcan to the curb every tuesday night How many jobs do you have.

One kind of worm from South america is eight feet long Have you ever seen such a huge worm, Yuck, Most worm are only a few inchs long. Some are less than a inch long

Unit 7 • Paragraph 27 Errors

Capitalization	1
Exclamation Points	1
Periods	2
Plurals	2
Question Marks	1
Usage	1

Total Errors: 8

Jane has many job around the house. She walks the dog twice a weeek. She washes the dishs after breakfast every saturday morning. She moves all three trashcan to the curb every tuesday night How many jobs do you have,

Unit 7 • Paragraph 28 Errors

Capitalization	2
Periods	1
Plurals	3
Question Marks	1
Spelling	1

Total Errors: 8

Name: ______________________ Date: ______________________

Josh had a dog that had five babys. His mom and dad said he could not keep all of the puppies? he sold two of the puppys. He gave two of the other to his freind. He kept one puppy

Unit 8
Paragraph
30

Raking leafs can be fun. jim puts a lot of leaf in a big pile. then he jumps into the big pile of leaves He laughs and rolls around. Then hee has to rake it all upp again.

Josh had a dog that had five ~~babys~~ [babies]. His mom and dad said he could not keep all of the puppies~~?~~ [delete ?]. [h → H] He sold two of the ~~puppys~~ [puppies]. He gave two of the other[s] to his ~~freind~~ [friend]. He kept one puppy[.]

Unit 8 • Paragraph 29
Errors

Capitalization	1
Periods	2
Plurals	3
Spelling	1

Total Errors: 7

Raking ~~leafs~~ [leaves] can be fun. [j → J] Jim puts a lot of ~~leaf~~ [leaves] in a big pile. [t → T] Then he jumps into the big pile of leaves[.] He laughs and rolls around. Then he~~e~~ [delete e] has to rake it all up~~p~~ [delete p] again.

Unit 8 • Paragraph 30
Errors

Capitalization	2
Periods	1
Plurals	2
Spelling	2

Total Errors: 7

Name: ______________________ Date: ______________

Have you ever seen a panda. Pandas are black and white. They have black spot over both of their eye. They have paws with five finger. Panda eat bamboo plants they also like to eat bugs eggs and fish.

Unit 8
Paragraph
32

Apples are, round, hard, and juicy. They can be red green or yellow. they grow high up in the branchs of trees. Fruits like apples are goood foods for you to eat. Would you like to eat a apple today.

Have you ever seen a panda. Pandas are black and white. They have black spot over both of their eye. They have paws with five finger. Panda eat bamboo plants they also like to eat bugs eggs and fish.

Unit 8 • Paragraph 31 Errors

Capitalization	1
Commas	2
Periods	1
Plurals	4
Question Marks	1

Total Errors: 9

Apples are, round, hard, and juicy. They can be red green or yellow. they grow high up in the branchs of trees. Fruits like apples are ~~gooood~~ good foods for you to eat. Would you like to eat ~~a~~ an apple today.

Unit 8 • Paragraph 32 Errors

Capitalization	1
Commas	3
Plurals	1
Question Marks	1
Spelling	1
Usage	1

Total Errors: 8

Name: ______________________ Date: ______________________

Tim's dog is named misty. Misty does not like to play with Tims toys. She would rather play with tims shoes. She chews on shoos. Tim thinks misty is funny. He gives her all of his shoe to chew. Misty is so happy?

Mom is having a Birthday party for Eva and her friends. All of her friends parents are coming, too. The party is starting at 230 Mom already baked the cake. Alll she has left to do is decorate the house with red green and yellow balloon.

Tim's dog is named misty. Misty does not like to play with Tims toys. She would rather play with tims shoes. She chews on shoos. Tim thinks misty is funny. He gives her all of his shoe to chew. Misty is so happy?

shoes

Unit 9 • Paragraph 33 Errors

Apostrophe	2
Capitalization	3
Exclamation Points	1
Plurals	1
Spelling	1

Total Errors: 8

Mom is having a Birthday party for Eva and her friends. All of her friends parents are coming, too. The party is starting at 230 Mom already baked the cake. Alll she has left to do is decorate the house with red green and yellow balloon.

Unit 9 • Paragraph 34 Errors

Apostrophe	1
Capitalization	1
Colons	1
Commas	2
Periods	1
Plurals	1
Spelling	1

Total Errors: 8

Name: ______________________ Date: ______________________

Elijah takes guitar lessons every thursday. Lessons always startt at 3:30 and go until 415. Elijahs teacher has already taught him how to play three song he said that Elijah is a quick learner?

We saww two beautiful butterflies in Baileys back yard. Their wing were orange black and white. Baileys mom said that the butterflys have been coming by all Summer. Bailey calls them her pets

Elijah takes guitar lessons every thursday. Lessons always startt at 3:30 and go until 415. Elijahs teacher has already taught him how to play three song he said that Elijah is a quick learner?

Unit 9 • Paragraph 35 Errors

Apostrophes	1
Capitalization	2
Colons	1
Periods	2
Plurals	1
Spelling	1

Total Errors: 8

We saww two beautiful butterflies in Baileys back yard. Their wing were orange black and white. Baileys mom said that the butterflys have been coming by all Summer. Bailey calls them her pets

Unit 9 • Paragraph 36 Errors

Apostrophes	2
Capitalization	1
Commas	2
Periods	1
Plurals	2
Spelling	1

Total Errors: 9

Name: ______________________ Date: ______________________

Davids parents just bought him a new glove a new bat and nu shoes. Monday is his first baseball game. Tim and me are going to watch him play David is very excited. Him said that his coachs and teammates are great.

A J asked if this tank of fish was yours. I told he that it was Uncle Tommys. Him has 10 tanks and over 100 fish. The fishs tanks are cleaned every tuesday. Uncle tommy knows a lot about fishes.

Davids parents just bought him a new glove a new bat and ~~nu~~ new shoes. Monday is his first baseball game. Tim and ~~me~~ I are going to watch him play David is very excited. ~~Him~~ He said that his coachs and teammates are great.

Unit 10 • Paragraph 37
Errors

Apostrophes	1
Commas	2
Periods	1
Plurals	1
Pronouns	2
Spelling	1

Total Errors: 8

A J asked if this tank of fish was yours. I told ~~he~~ him that it was Uncle Tommys. ~~Him~~ He has 10 tanks and over 100 fish. The fishs tanks are cleaned every tuesday. Uncle tommy knows a lot about fishes.

Unit 10 • Paragraph 38
Errors

Apostrophes	2
Capitalization	2
Periods	2
Plurals	1
Pronouns	2

Total Errors: 9

Name: ______________________________ Date: ____________________

Grandma's glass vase slipped from Amys hand. It hit the hard flor and broke into many piece. It was a old vase that had been in Amys home all her life Her felt very bad about breaking it.

Unit 10
Paragraph
40

Will Dr. Goss s son and daughter work in his office this summer. Both of his childs worked there last august. Them did a lot of job and were very helppful. He was very proud of they.

Grandma's glass vase slipped from Amys hand. It hit the hard flor and broke into many piece. It was a old vase that had been in Amys home all her life, Her felt very bad about breaking it.

Unit 10 • Paragraph 39 Errors

Apostrophes	2
Periods	1
Plurals	1
Pronouns	1
Spelling	1
Usage	1

Total Errors: 7

Will Dr. Goss s son and daughter work in his office this summer. Both of his childs worked there last august. Them did a lot of job and were very helppful. He was very proud of they.

Unit 10 • Paragraph 40 Errors

Apostrophes	1
Capitalization	1
Plurals	2
Pronouns	2
Question Marks	1
Spelling	1

Total Errors: 8

Name: ______________________ Date: ______________________

Mom want to bake a cake. I is old enough to help her now. I can git the eggs and the oil. i can help her stir the batter. I can help her eats the cake That is me favorite part!

It is hot in the Summer. You can swim in the watter to cool of. You can wear shorts T-shirts and sunglasses. You can play game outside like baseball and soccer. These things is fun. That is why everybody love summer.

Mom want^s^ to bake a cake. I ~~is~~ am old enough to help her now. I can ~~git~~ get the eggs and the oil. i can help her stir the batter. I can help her eats the cake. That is ~~me~~ my favorite part!

Unit 11 • Paragraph 41 Errors

Capitalization	1
Periods	1
Pronouns	1
Spelling	1
Verbs	3

Total Errors: 7

It is hot in the Summer. You can swim in the ~~watter~~ water to cool ~~of~~ off. You can wear shorts, T-shirts, and sunglasses. You can play game^s^ outside like baseball and soccer. These things ~~is~~ are fun. That is why everybody love^s^ summer.

Unit 11 • Paragraph 42 Errors

Capitalization	1
Commas	2
Plurals	1
Spelling	2
Verbs	2

Total Errors: 8

Name: ______________________ Date: ______________________

Ben haz to get a job. He likes to work with dogs. He also like to run for fun. What kind of a job do you think him should get. ben gots a job walking his neighbors dog. He likes his new jobb.

Unit 11
Paragraph
44

Kate want to skate. She is afraid to let go of her dads hand. Her dad tell her she can skate He smile at she. Kate lets go of he's hand. She is skating! her dad cheers.

Ben haz to get a job. He likes to work with dogs. He also like to run for fun. What kind of a job do you think him should get. ben gots a job walking his neighbors dog. He likes his new jobb.

Unit 11 • Paragraph 43 Errors

Error	Count
Apostrophes	1
Capitalization	1
Pronouns	1
Question Marks	1
Spelling	2
Verbs	2

Total Errors: 8

Kate want to skate. She is afraid to let go of her dads hand. Her dad tell her she can skate He smile at she. Kate lets go of he's hand. She is skating! her dad cheers.

Unit 11 • Paragraph 44 Errors

Error	Count
Apostrophes	1
Capitalization	1
Periods	1
Pronouns	2
Verbs	3

Total Errors: 8

Name: ______________________________ Date: ____________________

it was Marks job to give his dog a bath today. mark filled the bathtub with water. He scrubed the dog with soap. Then he rinse his dog. He did not hav to dry her off. She did that herself?

A seahorse is a odd fish. It move like a rocking horse Its head looks like a horses head. It wrapps its tail around things. I once touchd a seahorse. It wraped its tail around me finger!

it was Marks job to give his dog a bath today. mark filled the bathtub with water. He scrubed the dog with soap. Then he rinse his dog. He did not hav to dry her off. She did that herself?

Unit 12 • Paragraph 45 Errors

Apostrophes	1
Capitalization	2
Exclamation Points	1
Spelling	1
Verbs	2

Total Errors: 7

A seahorse is a odd fish. It move like a rocking horse Its head looks like a horses head. It wrapps its tail around things. I once touchd a seahorse. It wraped its tail around me finger!

Unit 12 • Paragraph 46 Errors

Apostrophes	1
Periods	1
Pronouns	1
Usage	1
Verbs	4

Total Errors: 8

Name: ______________________ Date: ______________________

Mom puts on her shoes and goes joging every morning. Our dog max joggs along with she. Mom say that runing is good for you. Dad jogged with mom and Max last saturday. It was his first time He did not like it.

Unit 12
Paragraph
48

Tammy Tommy and me are living with our grandparents this month. Dad is working in Austin texas for most of april. He calls we three every night to see how we are. He always tell us how much he missess us.

Mom puts on her shoes and goes joging every morning. Our dog max ~~joggs~~ jogs along with ~~she~~ her. Mom say that runing is good for you. Dad jogged with mom and Max last saturday. It was his first time He did not like it.

Unit 12 • Paragraph 47 Errors

Capitalization	3
Periods	1
Pronouns	1
Spelling	2
Verbs	2

Total Errors: 9

Tammy Tommy and ~~me~~ I are living with our grandparents this month. Dad is working in Austin texas for most of april. He calls ~~we~~ us three every night to see how we are. He always tell us how much he missess us.

Unit 12 • Paragraph 48 Errors

Capitalization	2
Commas	4
Pronouns	2
Spelling	1
Verbs	1

Total Errors: 10

Name: ______________________ Date: ______________________

Unit 13
Paragraph 49

Cindy thought she had lost her favorite stuffed animall. She look everywhere. She could not find Mr Bear. Cindy cryed for a long time Then she saw Mr. Bear! He was hideing unnder the bed. Mr. bear is silly.

Max is rideing the bus today. He trys to take it everry day. The bus was late yesterday, so max walked to school. The bus driver was sick. A new person is driveing the bus today. The new drivers name is Ms lacy

Cindy thought she had lost her favorite stuffed animall. She look everywhere. She could not find Mr Bear. Cindy cryed for a long time Then she saw Mr. Bear! He was hideing unnder the bed. Mr. bear is silly.

(Corrections marked: animall → animal; look → looked; Mr → Mr.; cryed → cried; time → time.; hideing → hiding; unnder → under; bear → Bear)

Unit 13 • Paragraph 49 Errors

Capitalization	1
Periods	2
Spelling	2
Verbs	3

Total Errors: 8

Max is rideing the bus today. He trys to take it everry day. The bus was late yesterday, so max walked to school. The bus driver was sick. A new person is driveing the bus today. The new drivers name is Ms lacy

(Corrections marked: rideing → riding; trys → tries; everry → every; max → Max; driveing → driving; drivers → driver's; Ms → Ms.; lacy → Lacy.)

Unit 13 • Paragraph 50 Errors

Apostrophes	1
Capitalization	2
Periods	2
Spelling	1
Verbs	3

Total Errors: 9

Name: ______________________ Date: ______________________

It was raining hard this morning Water was pour down out of the clouds. I gots soaking wet. Then the sun come out. It dryed my hair and my clothes. i saw two rainbow! It was a exciting dayy.

Mrs Wilks trys to exercise every day. She says that exercise is any action that gets you moveing. She runs bikes swims and jumps rope. Her and me are going swiming together this sunday.

It was raining hard this morning. Water was pouring down out of the clouds. I got soaking wet. Then the sun ~~come~~ came out. It ~~dryed~~ dried my hair and my clothes. I saw two rainbows! It was ~~a~~ an exciting day.

Unit 13 • Paragraph 51 Errors

Error	Count
Capitalization	1
Periods	1
Plurals	1
Spelling	1
Usage	1
Verbs	4

Total Errors: 9

Mrs. Wilks ~~trys~~ tries to exercise every day. She says that exercise is any action that gets you ~~moveing~~ moving. She runs, bikes, swims, and jumps rope. ~~Her~~ She and ~~me~~ I are going swimming together this Sunday.

Unit 13 • Paragraph 52 Errors

Error	Count
Capitalization	1
Commas	3
Periods	1
Pronouns	2
Verbs	3

Total Errors: 10

Name: ______________________________ Date: ____________________

sally saw a cat up in the tree It was stuck high up in the branchs. Sally runned to get her mother to help. Her mom getted a ladder and liftd the cat out of the tree. Sally was glad her could help the kat.

Unit 14
Paragraph
54

Dan go to a party yesterday for his friend. His friends name is Shelly. Dan gave shelly a presents. It was a umbrella. Shelly loved Dans present. She huggged him and thanked him for the umbrela.

sally saw a cat up in the tree It was stuck high up in the branchs. Sally ~~runned~~ ran to get her mother to help. Her mom ~~getted~~ got a ladder and liftd the cat out of the tree. Sally was glad ~~her~~ she could help the ~~kat.~~ cat

Unit 14 • Paragraph 53 Errors

Capitalization	1
Periods	1
Plurals	1
Pronouns	1
Spelling	1
Verbs	3

Total Errors: 8

Dan ~~go~~ went to a party yesterday for his friend. His friends name is Shelly. Dan gave shelly a presents. It was ~~a~~ an umbrella. Shelly loved Dans present. She ~~hugggged~~ hugged him and thanked him for the umbrela.

Unit 14 • Paragraph 54 Errors

Apostrophes	2
Capitalization	1
Plurals	1
Spelling	2
Usage	1
Verbs	1

Total Errors: 8

Name: ______________________________ Date: ____________________

We visited the Grand Canyon in arizona last Fall. A guide taked us down to the bottum. We rided a raft on the river down there. We has a great time at the grand canyon.

Unit 14
Paragraph
56

Can julian and i go to the beach on Friday? We go last week. We swimmed for hours. A orange crab crawled across my towel last friday. It scared Mom. Julian and me thinked that was funny.

We visited the Grand Canyon in arizona last Fall. A guide ~~taked~~ took us down to the ~~bottum.~~ bottom. We ~~rided~~ rode a raft on the river down there. We ~~has~~ had a great time at the grand canyon.

Unit 14 • Paragraph 55 Errors

Capitalization	4
Spelling	1
Verbs	3

Total Errors: 8

Can julian and i go to the beach on Friday? We ~~go~~ went last week. We ~~swimmed~~ swam for hours. ~~A~~ An orange crab crawled across my towel last friday. It scared Mom. Julian and ~~me~~ I ~~thinked~~ thought that was funny.

Unit 14 • Paragraph 56 Errors

Capitalization	3
Pronouns	1
Usage	1
Verbs	3

Total Errors: 8

Name: ______________________ Date: ______________________

Make sure to take care of your tooths. Brush them after every meal Floss them each knight. U should also visit your dentist too times each year. This help give you a beautiful smile

Pat eated a pear. She found a seed. She came up with a idea. She plant the seed in the dirt. She maked sure the plant got watter and sunlight. pat hopes that the seed will become a big pare tree won day.

Make sure to take care of your ~~tooths.~~ teeth Brush them after every meal. Floss them each knight. ~~U~~ You should also visit your dentist ~~too~~ two times each year. This help^s give you a beautiful smile.

Unit 15 • Paragraph 57 Errors

Homophones	2
Periods	2
Plurals	1
Spelling	1
Verbs	1

Total Errors: 7

Pat ~~eated~~ ate a pear. She found a seed. She came up with ~~a~~ an idea. She plant^ed the seed in the dirt. She ~~maked~~ made sure the plant got ~~watter~~ water and sunlight. pat hopes that the seed will become a big ~~pare~~ pear tree ~~won~~ one day.

Unit 15 • Paragraph 58 Errors

Capitalization	1
Homophones	2
Spelling	1
Usage	1
Verbs	3

Total Errors: 8

Name: ______________________ Date: ______________________

It was a cloudy day in the Month of may. Sally weared a coat gloves and a scarf. She new that it would be cold. It started to rein. Sally wished she had bringed a umbrella.

I has four brother. All fore of my brothers names begin with the same letter. Their names is Bobby billy Buddy, and brad. Bobby is the oldest. He is ate years older than I am.

It was a cloudy day in the Month of may. Sally ~~weared~~ wore a coat, gloves, and a scarf. She knew that it would be cold. It started to ~~rein.~~ rain Sally wished she had ~~bringed~~ brought ~~a~~ an umbrella.

Unit 15 • Paragraph 59 Errors

Capitalization	2
Commas	2
Homophones	2
Usage	1
Verbs	2

Total Errors: 9

I ~~has~~ have four brothers. All ~~fore~~ four of my brothers' names begin with the same letter. Their names ~~is~~ are Bobby, billy, Buddy, and brad. Bobby is the oldest. He is ~~ate~~ eight years older than I am.

Unit 15 • Paragraph 60 Errors

Apostrophes	1
Capitalization	2
Commas	2
Homophones	2
Plurals	1
Verbs	2

Total Errors: 10

Name: ____________________ Date: ____________________

Teva and julia are best freinds They likes to ski in the mountains. They go to the mountains every febuary to ski. What dew you like to do when it snows.

Unit 16
Paragraph
62

There are fore oceans on Earth. They is the Pacific the atlantic, the indian, and the Arctic. Have you ever tasted ocean water. It is two salty to drink. Drinking salt water can make you vary sick.

Teva and julia are best ~~freinds~~ friends They likes to ski in the mountains. They go to the mountains every febuary to ski. What ~~dew~~ do you like to do when it snows.

Unit 16 • Paragraph 61 Errors

Capitalization	2
Homophones	1
Periods	1
Question Marks	1
Spelling	2
Verbs	1

Total Errors: 8

There are ~~fore~~ four oceans on Earth. They ~~is~~ are the Pacific the atlantic, the indian, and the Arctic. Have you ever tasted ocean water. It is ~~two~~ too salty to drink. Drinking salt water can make you ~~vary~~ very sick.

Unit 16 • Paragraph 62 Errors

Capitalization	2
Commas	1
Homophones	3
Question Marks	1
Verbs	1

Total Errors: 8

Name: ______________________________ Date: ____________________

Fruits and vegetable come in many colors. Can you think of a few. There are red berrys, orange carrots, and green peppers. Blueberrys are blew. Grapes can be red purple black or green.

Unit 16
Paragraph
64

All plants need water air and light. plants do not eat. They use the lite from the sun to make their own food. Plants make the food in their leafs. Then they store the food in there stems and roots. Them use this food on gloomy day when the son does not shine.

Fruits and vegetable^s come in many colors. Can you think of a few? There are red ~~berrys~~ berries, orange carrots, and green peppers. ~~Blueberrys~~ Blueberries are ~~blew~~ blue. Grapes can be red, purple, black, or green.

Unit 16 • Paragraph 63 Errors

Commas........ 3
Homophones 1
Plurals 3
Question Marks 1

Total Errors: 8

All plants need water, air, and light. Plants do not eat. They use the ~~lite~~ light from the sun to make their own food. Plants make the food in their ~~leafs~~ leaves. Then they store the food in ~~there~~ their stems and roots. ~~Them~~ They use this food on gloomy day^s when the ~~son~~ sun does not shine.

Unit 16 • Paragraph 64 Errors

Capitalization 1
Commas........ 2
Homophones 2
Plurals 2
Pronouns 1
Spelling 1

Total Errors: 9

Name: ______________________ Date: ______________________

the ocean give us fish for food. It lets us sale boats from one places to another place. we can even surf on ocean waves. Doo you like swimming in the ocean.

Unit 17
Paragraph
66

We learned about penguins today These penguin cannot fly. Them can dive and swim. they can also walk many mile over ice and sno. These penguins live inn a cold place called antarctica.

the ocean give^s us fish for food. It lets us ~~sale~~ sail boats from one places to another place. we can even surf on ocean waves. Doo you like swimming in the ocean. ?

Unit 17 • Paragraph 65 Errors

Capitalization	2
Homophones	1
Plurals	1
Question Marks	1
Spelling	1
Verbs	1

Total Errors: 7

We learned about penguins today. These penguin^s cannot fly. ~~Them~~ They can dive and swim. they can also walk many mile^s over ice and sno^w. These penguins live inn a cold place called antarctica.

Unit 17 • Paragraph 66 Errors

Capitalization	2
Homophones	1
Periods	1
Plurals	2
Pronouns	1
Spelling	1

Total Errors: 8

Name: ______________________ Date: ______________________

Luke plays Soccer in the Summer. He likes dribbling the ball He like kicking it. he likes passing the ball too his frends. His favorite part is scoreing a goal.

Dan likes to play with cars. Sam like to play with blocks Sam make a road with his blocks. Dan give Sam a car. dan and sam play with their cars on the rode.

Luke plays Soccer in the Summer. He likes dribbling the ball He like kicking it. he likes passing the ball too his frends. His favorite part is ~~scoreing~~ scoring a goal.

Unit 17 • Paragraph 67
Errors

Capitalization	3
Homophones	1
Periods	1
Spelling	1
Verbs	2

Total Errors: 8

Dan likes to play with cars. Sam like to play with blocks Sam make a road with his blocks. Dan give Sam a car. dan and sam play with their cars on the ~~rode.~~ road

Unit 17 • Paragraph 68
Errors

Capitalization	2
Homophones	1
Periods	1
Verbs	3

Total Errors: 7

Name: ______________________ Date: ______________________

Unit 18 Paragraph 69

A desert is hot and dry. Very little rein falls in a desert That is why there is knot much water in the desert. Each days the son heats up the dessert. Then at night the desert get very cold.

Unit 18 Paragraph 70

Did you know that light can bend. When it does, it makes a color. This is why wee see rainbow. Rainbows are maked up of red, orange yellow, green, blue indigo, and violet.

A desert is hot and dry. Very little ~~rein~~ rain falls in a desert That is why there is knot much water in the desert. Each days the ~~son~~ sun heats up the ~~dessert.~~ desert Then at night the desert get s very cold.

Unit 18 • Paragraph 69
Errors

Homophones	4
Plurals	1
Periods	1
Verbs	1

Total Errors: 7

Did you know that light can bend. ?
When it does, it makes a color. This is why wee see rainbow s. Rainbows are ~~maked~~ made up of red, orange yellow, green, blue indigo, and violet.

Unit 18 • Paragraph 70
Errors

Commas	2
Homophones	1
Plurals	1
Question Marks	1
Verbs	1

Total Errors: 6

Name: ______________________________ Date: ____________________

Bob wares a wig. He puts on big shoe and silly clothes. He paints his face with makeup Then he goes to work. He make childs laugh. What job do you think bob has

Sue could here meowing. She walked over to the tree and looked up Do you know what was in the tree. It was a scared kat. Sue helped the cat get down. She give it sum milk.

Bob ~~wares~~ wears a wig. He puts on big shoe^s and silly clothes. He paints his face with makeup. Then he goes to work. He make^s ~~childs~~ children laugh. What job do you think Bob has?

Unit 18 • Paragraph 71 Errors

Capitalization	1
Homophones	1
Periods	1
Plurals	2
Question Marks	1
Verbs	1

Total Errors: 7

Sue could ~~here~~ hear meowing. She walked over to the tree and looked up. Do you know what was in the tree? It was a scared ~~kat.~~ cat. Sue ~~helpped~~ helped the cat get down. She ~~give~~ gave it ~~sum~~ some milk.

Unit 18 • Paragraph 72 Errors

Homophones	2
Periods	1
Question Marks	1
Spelling	1
Verbs	2

Total Errors: 7

Name: ______________________________ Date: ____________________

A mountain is a very tall hill. There are mountain all over the world. The talllest mountain in the world is called Mount everest. It is in the country of nepal. Peeple climb to its top. It is very cold?

would you like to visit a diamond mine. There is a mine in arkansas. It is a state park. You can dig for diamonds at this park. Dimonds are worth a lott of money. What would you do if you finded one.

A mountain is a very tall hill. There are mountain all over the world. The talllest mountain in the world is called Mount everest. It is in the country of nepal. Peeple climb to its top. It is very cold?

s | tallest | People

Unit 19 • Paragraph 73 Errors

Capitalization	2
Periods	1
Plurals	1
Spelling	2

Total Errors: 6

would you like to visit a diamond mine. There is a mine in arkansas. It is a state park. You can dig for diamonds at this park. Dimonds are worth a lott of money. What would you do if you finded one.

? | a | found | ?

Unit 19 • Paragraph 74 Errors

Capitalization	2
Question Marks	2
Spelling	2
Verbs	1

Total Errors: 7

Name: ______________________ Date: ______________

We flied on a airplane to see Grandpa Joe. It was grandpa Joes birthday. He turned 80 on october 9. He live in Dallas Texas. It was so much fun

Unit 19 Paragraph 76

We see fireworks on the Fourth of july. There are many parade. Familys spend the day together. Most people has the day of. Why do they have the day off. It is Americas birthday.

We ~~flied~~ flew on ~~a~~ an airplane to see Grandpa Joe. It was grandpa Joe's birthday. He turned 80 on october 9. He lives in Dallas, Texas. It was so much fun!

Unit 19 • Paragraph 75
Errors

Error type	Count
Apostrophes	1
Capitalization	2
Commas	1
Exclamation Points	1
Usage	1
Verbs	2

Total Errors: 8

We see fireworks on the Fourth of july. There are many parades. ~~Familys~~ Families spend the day together. Most people ~~has~~ have the day off. Why do they have the day off? It is America's birthday.

Unit 19 • Paragraph 76
Errors

Error type	Count
Apostrophes	1
Capitalization	1
Plurals	2
Question Marks	1
Spelling	1
Verbs	1

Total Errors: 7

Name: ______________________ Date: ______________________

Lakes and rivvers hold fresh water. Rain snow and ice are forms of fresh water. Plants, animalls, and people need fresh water? Without watter, their would be no life on earth.

Unit 20
Paragraph
78

a sea otter like to float on its back. It can eat on it's back. It can sleep that way, to. It can carry its babys on its back Baby otters is called pups.

Lakes and ~~rivvers~~ rivers hold fresh water. Rain, snow, and ice are forms of fresh water. Plants, ~~animalls~~ animals, and people need fresh water? . Without ~~watter~~ water, ~~their~~ there would be no life on earth. (E)

Unit 20 • Paragraph 77 Errors

Capitalization	1
Commas	2
Homophones	1
Periods	1
Spelling	3

Total Errors: 8

a (A) sea otter like^s to float on its back. It can eat on ~~it's~~ its back. It can sleep that way, to^o. It can carry its ~~babys~~ babies on its back. Baby otters ~~is~~ are called pups.

Unit 20 • Paragraph 78 Errors

Capitalization	1
Homophones	2
Periods	1
Plurals	1
Verbs	2

Total Errors: 7

Name: ______________________ Date: ______________

I go to bed the same way every knight. I begin bye brushing my tooths and washing my face. Then Mom tuck me into bed She reads me a story, and i get sleepy. Then mom kisses me goodnight.

Unit 20
Paragraph
80

There are many thing to know about owls. They eat mice, frogs, snakes insects, and small birds They can fly without makeing a sound. They can sea and here very well. They do their huntting at night.

I go to bed the same way every knight. I begin bye brushing my teeth ~~tooths~~ and washing my face. Then Mom tuck^s me into bed. She reads me a story, and i get sleepy. Then mom kisses me goodnight.

Unit 20 • Paragraph 79 Errors

Capitalization	2
Homophones	2
Periods	1
Plurals	1
Verbs	1

Total Errors: 7

There are many thing^s to know about owls. They eat mice, frogs, snakes, insects, and small birds. They can fly without making ~~makeing~~ a sound. They can see ~~sea~~ and hear ~~here~~ very well. They do their hunting ~~huntting~~ at night.

Unit 20 • Paragraph 80 Errors

Commas	1
Homophones	2
Periods	1
Plurals	1
Spelling	1
Verbs	1

Total Errors: 7

Name: ______________________ Date: ______________________

Ben has a pet dog. His dogs name is Max. Max likes to play ball with ben. Max allso likes to eat treets. Ben likes to take max for walks. Ben love his dog

Katie likes to swim in her poool. Her can dive and make a big spplash. Katie also like to swim with her sister. Her name is Kelly. katie and kelly always have fun swiming together.

Ben has a pet dog. His dogs name is Max. Max likes to play ball with ben. Max ~~allso~~ also likes to eat ~~treets~~ treats. Ben likes to take max for walks. Ben love[s] his dog

Unit 21 • Paragraph 81 Errors

Apostrophes	1
Capitalization	2
Periods	1
Spelling	2
Verbs	1

Total Errors: 7

Katie likes to swim in her ~~poool~~ pool. ~~Her~~ She can dive and make a big ~~spplash~~ splash. Katie also like[s] to swim with her sister. Her name is Kelly. katie and kelly always have fun swim[m]ing together.

Unit 21 • Paragraph 82 Errors

Capitalization	2
Pronouns	1
Spelling	2
Verbs	2

Total Errors: 7

Name: ______________________ Date: ______________________

Unit 21
Paragraph 83

I baked a cake in are oven. I maked a mistake. The cake did not taste write. I forgetted to put sugar in me cake. I ate the cake anyway That was the second mistake i made that day.

The polar bear lives in a cold and icy place called the arctic. How do a polar bare do that? How does it not freeze. Polar bears have very thick fir. They also have a thick layer of fat that protect them from the cold

I baked a cake in ~~are~~ our oven. I ~~maked~~ made a mistake. The cake did not taste ~~write~~ right. I ~~forgetted~~ forgot to put sugar in ~~me~~ my cake. I ate the cake anyway. That was the second mistake i made that day.

Unit 21 • Paragraph 83
Errors

Capitalization 1
Homophones 2
Periods 1
Pronouns 1
Verbs 2

Total Errors: 7

The polar bear lives in a cold and icy place called the arctic. How do^es^ a polar ~~bare~~ bear do that? How does it not freeze? Polar bears have very thick ~~fir~~ fur. They also have a thick layer of fat that protect^s^ them from the cold.

Unit 21 • Paragraph 84
Errors

Capitalization 1
Homophones 2
Periods 1
Question
Marks. 1
Verbs 2

Total Errors: 7

Name: ______________________ Date: ______________

Walt and me are best friends. We meeted when we was in kindergarten. We both liked the color purpel. Us both liked the same sports. Our moms said that we was like two pea in a pod.

Unit 22
Paragraph
86

I have a pet bird named fred He is a parrot. Fred has blew and yellow feather. He can say elevven words. I will teech him to say more. I like haveing a pet who can talk?

Walt and ~~me~~ I are best friends. We ~~meeted~~ met when we ~~was~~ were in kindergarten. We both liked the color ~~purpel~~ purple. ~~Us~~ We both liked the same sports. Our moms said that we ~~was~~ were like two pea^s in a pod.

Unit 22 • Paragraph 85 Errors

Plurals	1
Pronouns	2
Spelling	1
Verbs	3

Total Errors: 7

I have a pet bird named fred He is a parrot. Fred has ~~blew~~ blue and yellow feather^s. He can say ~~elevven~~ eleven words. I will ~~teech~~ teach him to say more. I like ~~haveing~~ having a pet who can talk?

Unit 22 • Paragraph 86 Errors

Capitalization	1
Homophones	1
Periods	2
Plurals	1
Spelling	2
Verbs	1

Total Errors: 8

Name: ______________________________ Date: ____________________

Emma's nephew was born on june 30 2010, at 832 p m Her nephews name is Alex. Emma can still remember that day. She cryed and smiled at the same time. Alex is much biger now.

Unit 22
Paragraph
88

The farmers sons picked apples plums and peachs from his orchard. They did this for six ours straight. It was hard work The farmer gived them each fifty dollars and two barrel of fruit.

Emma's nephew was born on june 30 2010, at 832 p m Her nephews name is Alex. Emma can still remember that day. She ~~cryed~~ cried and smiled at the same time. Alex is much ~~biger~~ bigger now.

Unit 22 • Paragraph 87 Errors

Apostrophes 1
Capitalization 1
Colons 1
Commas 1
Periods 2
Spelling 1
Verbs 1

Total Errors: 8

The farmers sons picked apples plums and peachs from his orchard. They did this for six ours straight. It was hard work The farmer ~~gived~~ gave them each fifty dollars and two barrel of fruit.

Unit 22 • Paragraph 88 Errors

Apostrophes 1
Commas 2
Homophones 1
Periods 1
Plurals 2
Verbs 1

Total Errors: 8

Name: ____________________ Date: ____________________

There is a famous tower in Paris france. It is called the eiffel Tower. It taked about too years to built this famous tower. It was completed on March 31 1889. Have you ever seen it.

Unit 23
Paragraph 89

The state of wyoming was the first to have a woman governor. That governors name was nellie T Ross. Her was elected on November 4 1924. Mrs ross lived to be 101 year old.

Unit 23
Paragraph 90

There is a famous tower in Paris france. It is called the eiffel Tower. It ~~taked~~ took about ~~too~~ two years to ~~built~~ build this famous tower. It was completed on March 31 1889. Have you ever seen it.

Unit 23 • Paragraph 89
Errors

Capitalization	2
Commas	2
Homophones	1
Question Marks	1
Verbs	2
Total Errors:	8

The state of wyoming was the first to have a woman governor. That governors name was nellie T Ross. ~~Her~~ She was elected on November 4 1924. Mrs ross lived to be 101 year old.

Unit 23 • Paragraph 90
Errors

Apostrophes	1
Capitalization	3
Commas	1
Periods	2
Plurals	1
Pronouns	1
Total Errors:	9

Name: ______________________________ Date: ____________________

Unit 23 Paragraph 91

Sophia loves to bake cookie. Her mother helps her mixx the dough. Sophia scoops the doe onto cookie sheets. Then sophia puts the cookys in the oven. She let them bake until they is gooey and delishus.

Unit 23 Paragraph 92

Mom waked me up early on saturday morning. She telled me to take a look outside. I was still in me pajamas. I saw something in are driveway. It was a nu bicycle. What a grate day?

Sophia loves to bake cookie. Her mother helps her mixx the dough. Sophia scoops the doe onto cookie sheets. Then sophia puts the cookys in the oven. She let them bake until they is gooey and delishus.

Corrections: cookie → cookies; mixx → mix; doe → dough; sophia → Sophia; cookys → cookies; let → lets; is → are; delishus → delicious

Unit 23 • Paragraph 91 Errors

Capitalization 1
Homophones 1
Plurals 1
Spelling 3
Verbs 2

Total Errors: 8

Mom waked me up early on saturday morning. She telled me to take a look outside. I was still in me pajamas. I saw something in are driveway. It was a nu bicycle. What a grate day?

Corrections: waked → woke; saturday → Saturday; telled → told; me → my; are → our; nu → new; grate → great; ? → !

Unit 23 • Paragraph 92 Errors

Capitalization 1
Exclamation Points. 1
Homophones 2
Pronouns 1
Spelling 1
Verbs 2

Total Errors: 8

Name: ______________________________ Date: ____________________

Unit 24
Paragraph 93

Carla tripped and falled down the stares. She hurt her leg. We were afrayed that she might have broken it. We take her to see Dr wilson. He sayed it was only bruised. She was fine after a few day.

Unit 24
Paragraph 94

It is Janes job to set the table. She do this each night. She sets out the glasses. She sets out the dishs. She set out the forks the knifes and the spoons. jane always forget the napkins!

Carla tripped and ~~falled~~ fell down the ~~stares~~ stairs. She hurt her leg. We were ~~afrayed~~ afraid that she might have broken it. We ~~take~~ took her to see Dr[.] wilson. He ~~sayed~~ said it was only bruised. She was fine after a few day[s].

Unit 24 • Paragraph 93 Errors

Error	Count
Capitalization	1
Homophones	1
Periods	1
Plurals	1
Spelling	1
Verbs	3

Total Errors: 8

It is Jane[']s job to set the table. She do[es] this each night. She sets out the glasses. She sets out the dish[e]s. She set[s] out the forks[,] the ~~knifes~~ knives[,] and the spoons. jane always forget[s] the napkins!

Unit 24 • Paragraph 94 Errors

Error	Count
Apostrophes	1
Capitalization	1
Commas	2
Plurals	2
Verbs	3

Total Errors: 9

Name: ______________________ Date: ______________________

Unit 24
Paragraph 95

Tim, kim, and i went to Main st Mall last Friday. We got to shop for a extra hour that day. Dads car gots a flat tire on the weigh to pick us up. He fixd the tire and then come to get us.

We spended all day at the zoo. We saw lions tigers and monkeys. We saw a elephant spraying water with its trunk. We seen a Giraffe eating from the branchs of a tall tree We saw many amazing annimals.

Tim, kim, and i went to Main st Mall last Friday. We got to shop for a extra hour that day. Dads car gots a flat tire on the weigh to pick us up. He fixd the tire and then come to get us.

(Corrections: an; way; e; came)

Unit 24 • Paragraph 95
Errors

Apostrophes	1
Capitalization	3
Homophones	1
Periods	1
Usage	1
Verbs	3

Total Errors: 10

We spended all day at the zoo. We saw lions tigers and monkeys. We saw a elephant spraying water with its trunk. We seen a Giraffe eating from the branchs of a tall tree We saw many amazing annimals.

(Corrections: spent; an; saw; e; animals)

Unit 24 • Paragraph 96
Errors

Capitalization	1
Commas	2
Periods	1
Plurals	1
Spelling	1
Usage	1
Verbs	2

Total Errors: 9

Name: ______________________ Date: ______________

The fox had three boxs. He gived one box to the dog. What was inside the box. It was a friendly frog. The frog hoped onto the dogs lap. The dog liked his knew pet frog. he named it hoppy.

Mom packed both of are lunches. She gave us each a sandwich and a orange. She pact a small bag of pretzels in Jennys lunch and a bag of cracker in mine. She get two juice boxs from the fridge and gived us each one

The fox had three boxs. He gived one box to the dog. What was inside the box. It was a friendly frog. The frog hoped onto the dogs lap. The dog liked his knew pet frog. he named it hoppy.

e, gave, ?, p, '

Unit 25 • Paragraph 97
Errors

Apostrophes..... 1
Capitalization 2
Homophones 1
Plurals 1
Question Marks......... 1
Verbs 2

Total Errors: 8

Mom packed both of are lunches. She gave us each a sandwich and a orange. She pact a small bag of pretzels in Jennys lunch and a bag of cracker in mine. She get two juice boxs from the fridge and gived us each one

our, an, packed, ', s, got, e, gave

Unit 25 • Paragraph 98
Errors

Apostrophes..... 1
Homophones 2
Periods......... 1
Plurals 2
Usage 1
Verbs 2

Total Errors: 9

Name: ______________________________ Date: ____________________

it is sayed that one song is sung more than others What is the song. It is "Happy Birthday to You." This song is singed all overr the world. It is not allways sung in english. It is sung in different languages, to.

Unit 25
Paragraph
100

Mrs martin always make us think. She asks us qwestions. Today she showwed us pictures of three thing. She asked us how they was alike. The three things were a cat a chicken and a coat. I new that all three words started with the same letter.

it is ~~sayed~~ said that one song is sung more than others. What is the song? It is "Happy Birthday to You." This song is ~~singed~~ sung all over the world. It is not ~~allways~~ always sung in english. It is sung in different languages, too.

Unit 25 • Paragraph 99 Errors

Capitalization	2
Homophones	1
Periods	1
Question Marks	1
Spelling	2
Verbs	2

Total Errors: 9

Mrs. martin always makes us think. She asks us ~~qwestions~~ questions. Today she ~~showwed~~ showed us pictures of three things. She asked us how they ~~was~~ were alike. The three things were a cat, a chicken, and a coat. I knew that all three words started with the same letter.

Unit 25 • Paragraph 100 Errors

Capitalization	1
Commas	2
Homophones	1
Periods	1
Plurals	1
Spelling	2
Verbs	2

Total Errors: 10

Editing Marks

Here is a list of the editing marks that are used in this book.

Mark	Meaning	Example
≡	Capitalize	We visited france.
/	Lowercase	It is Summer.
^	Insert	We at tacos today.
ℓ	Delete	I likes that movie.
⊙	Add Period	I am here
?	Add Question Mark	Who is it
!	Add Exclamation Point	Watch out
⦶	Add Comma	He lives in Ames Iowa.
:	Add Colon	I woke up at 630.
'	Add Apostrophe	That is Bobs hat.